Public Speaking for Kids

Written by Charlotte Jaffe and Barbara Doherty
Cover Illustrated by Koryn Agnello
Text Illustrated by Karen Sigler and Koryn Agnello

ISBN 1-56644-034-3

EDUCATIONAL IMPRESSIONS, INC.
Hawthorne, NJ 07507

Printed in the United States of America.

Table of Contents

OVERVIEW 5–6

SECTION I: THE FIRST STEPS 7–21
- Using Your Voice Correctly 8–9
- Body Language 10
- Eye Contact 11
- Facial Expressions 12
- Inflection and Speed 13
- Getting Attention 14
- Expert Tips 15
- Evaluate the Experts 16
- Peer-/Self-Evaluation Checklist 17
- Framing Your Speech: The Main Parts of a Speech 18
- A Sample Speech 19
- Using Note Cards 20
- Using an Outline 21
- Just Before Speaking… 22
- Pick a Prompt: Topics for Speaking 23–24

SECTION II: PUTTING IT INTO PRACTICE 25–53
- Choral Speaking: Famous Poetry 26
- Choral Speaking: Famous Speeches 27
- Creative Dramatics 28
- Speech Planning Form 29
- All About Me 30
- Sharing Your Own Experiences 31
- Oral Description 32
- On the Air (School Newscasters) 33
- Let's Debate 34
- Making Introductions 35
- Old-Time Radio Shows 36
- Ad Campaign Presentation 37
- Ad Campaign Presentation: Create a TV Commercial 38
- Photo Fun 39
- A Day in the Life of a Community Helper 40
- Teacher for a Day 41
- Story Villains Speak Out 42
- How to Conduct a Meeting 43
- Persuasive Speaking 44
- How-to Talks 45
- Giving Directions to a Location 46
- Television Review 47
- Just for Fun! 48

Storytelling 49
An Election Campaign Speech 50
Celebrity Interview..51
A Classroom Museum 52
Personal Treasures 53
Current Events 54
A Special Someone 55
Cause and Effect 56

SECTION IV: ALL AROUND TOWN 57–64
Choosing a Site 58
Gathering Information 59
Planning Your Speech 60
Your Tour Guide Speech 61
You're Invited: A Sample Invitation 62
Tour Guide Certificate of Participation 63
Evaluation Form..64

Overview

Public Speaking for Kids was designed to help teachers teach youngsters the basic elements of good speaking and to instill in them a sense of confidence as they communicate orally with others. The book is divided into three sections: The First Steps, Putting It into Practice, and All Around Town.

SECTION I: THE FIRST STEPS

Students are presented with the basic elements of good speaking. They learn to use their voices correctly and to apply eye contact, body language, and facial expressions in the proper manner. Tips on varied ways to prepare for oral presentations are given. Evaluation checklists provide guidance and quick reference. The Pick a Prompt activity offers students an opportunity to use the knowledge they have learned in a fun way.

SECTION II: PUTTING IT INTO PRACTICE

This section offers a variety of speaking experiences, both formal and informal, for solo or group presentations. By participating in these activities, students will learn to use oral language for various purposes and for various audiences. Students will gain poise and become more confident about speaking in front of a group. They will also learn to write speeches and to prepare for oral assignments in the correct way.

SECTION III: ALL AROUND TOWN

This unique culminating activity focuses on the students' own community. Parents, teachers, other classes, and administrators will be invited to attend the event. After researching important sites within their community, students will develop talks about these interesting places. Using well-prepared speeches, students will act as tour guides and take the audience on a journey "all around the town." Certificates will be awarded to participants, and the guided tours will be evaluated.

SECTION I

The First Steps

Using Your Voice Correctly

When you speak, it is essential to use your voice to its best advantage. The chart below gives a few points to keep in mind when presenting a speech.

PRESENTING A SPEECH EFFECTIVELY

- Speak audibly and vary the volume of your voice. Try to keep it from becoming too loud or too soft.
- Speak with appropriate expression in your voice. Keep your audience interested. If you speak in a monotonous tone, your audience may become bored.
- Emphasize certain words or segments of the speech in order to make a particular point, inject humor, or create excitement or sympathy.
- Control the pacing of your speech. Do not speak too quickly or too slowly. Make effective use of pauses.
- Pronounce your words clearly and correctly. It is as important to hear the last syllable of a word as it is to hear the first.

Using Your Voice Correctly: Be a Sportscaster

Pretend that you are a sportscaster. Describe a game that your class plays during physical education period. Write your sports commentary in the space below. Underline words that need to be emphasized when you present it orally to your class. On your paper, indicate the places where you may want to pause, speak loudly, speak softly, speak quickly, or speak slowly.

Body Language

Good body language is an essential part of every successful oral presentation. Here are some tips to follow:

1. Stand straight and tall. It is often distracting to the audience when the speaker leans or slumps during the speech.

2. Gestures or hand movements can provide added expression or emphasis to your talk. The use of gestures must be appropriate, natural, and meaningful. Gestures are often used to help you relate an emotional part of your speech. The following are some examples of gesturing: shaking your fist to show anger and wiping your eyes to show sadness.

3. Eliminate hand-wringing and other nervous gestures. These actions can take the audience's attention away from the main elements of your speech.

For this activity, you will work with a partner. Read the following statements. How would you interpret them with gestures? Take turns with your partner. Compare your interpretations.

1. I've told you before. I will not baby-sit for Billy again!

2. Look out! There's a car on your right!

3. Stand back until I open the door.

4. Why should I listen to your advice?

5. It's okay to enter the old house now. Follow me.

6. This movie is scary! I'm afraid to look.

7. Oh, no! We just missed our flight.

8. Let's be friends.

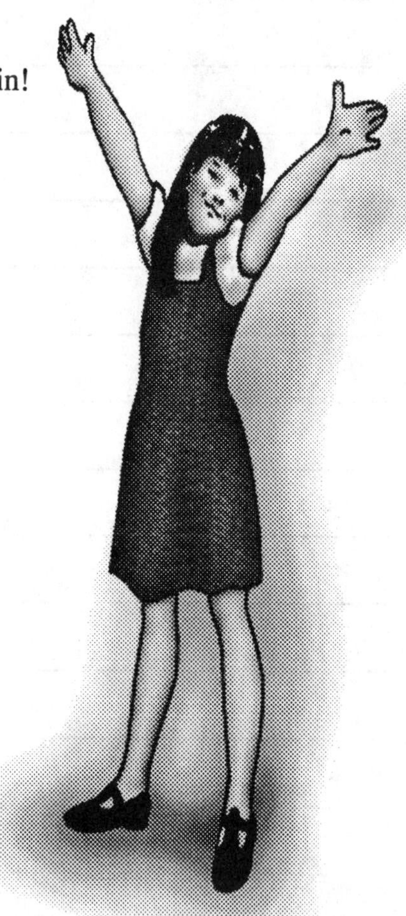

Eye Contact

Making eye contact with your audience is very important. Just think how you feel when a person who is speaking to you doesn't look at you. How do you feel? Do you wonder if the speaker is being dishonest or insincere? You may wonder if the speaker cares whether you are listening or not!

When giving a speech to a group, you may not be able to make eye contact with every listener in the audience. It is still important to look at the audience. Use a scanning gaze in the same way that you would pan the rows with a videocamera. Make quick glimpses of your note cards or outline and then look back at your listeners. Very often a speaker will focus on someone or something in the back of the room, such as a clock, a banner, a flag, or a photograph. You will want to avoid making direct eye contact if you think that it will cause you to lose your composure.

Use these techniques to practice making eye contact:

- Practice in front of a mirror. Be aware of how much time is spent looking down at your outline or notes and how much time is focused on the listeners.

- Have someone videotape you giving a two-minute speech.

- Working with a partner, alternate giving a short speech and evaluating your partner's speech for eye contact.

Facial Expressions

While you are speaking, you can also be communicating by the use of your facial expressions. Think of the ways faces look in anger, surprise, happiness, and sadness. You can sometimes tell if a person is in pain, is tense, or is relaxed just by noting his or her facial expression.

The most important facial expression you will want to remember is a smile. A smile conveys friendliness. It will help put yourself and your listeners at ease. Just as you would greet someone you meet with a smile, greet your audience, too, with a smile. Smiles can also come in handy if you make a mistake—simply smile, apologize, and continue with your speech.

Of course, if you are speaking about a very serious issue, you will not want to smile inappropriately. For example, you would not want to smile while reporting some sort of devastation or tragedy. Neither would you want to smile while giving a eulogy or taking an oath of office.

It is all right to laugh at yourself if you make an obvious mistake or if something happens that is out of your control: there is a power failure; a breeze blows away your note cards; the lectern and/or the microphone are not set at the correct height; or a bell rings right in the middle of a sentence. Try to smile in the face of these disturbances and be natural. Do not let them upset you!

Make sure that you can read and understand your note cards or outline easily. If you cannot, you may unknowingly make faces or squint while trying to read them.

Remember to check yourself in a mirror and on videotape.

Inflection and Speed

Inflection

How you emphasize certain words or word parts can make a big difference in your speaking and reading. In some cases, the emphasis can actually signify a change in meaning. Here are some phrases and sentences for you to practice:

I WILL

"I will." (with politeness)
"I will." (with anger and resentment)
"I will!" (with enthusiasm and excitement)
"I will?" (with confusion)

ANDREW'S PET

"This is Andrew's pet." (pointing to a gerbil)
"This is Andrew's pet." (pointing to a tiger)

POLITE OR RUDE?

You have heard some phrases or expressions of politeness that are given a different meaning by the way they were spoken in certain circumstances. Try these. See if you can change the meanings of these polite expressions by the way you say them.

Thank you.
Excuse me.
After you.
I'm sorry.
Pardon me.

Speed

The speed at which you speak can make a difference in how well you are understood and how difficult or easy it is for the listener to follow and get your message. In a conversation, the speakers alternate. Each speaker has a chance to absorb the other's comments. In a speech, however, it is more difficult to absorb the speaker's comments. You must, therefore, speak more slowly when giving a speech than when taking part in a conversation.

Most people have a tendency to deliver an oral presentation much too quickly. In an effort to "get through it," the speaker often rushes. When reading written work, we pause at commas, semi-colons, periods, and other punctuation marks. An effective speaker must also pause to emphasize certain points of the message and to give listeners a chance to absorb what is said.

PRACTICE: Tape record yourself reading a few paragraphs as you normally would. Listen to yourself. Exchange tapes with a partner. Critique each other.

Getting Attention

Part of being a good public speaker is having the attention of the listeners. In order to get the attention of a group it is often necessary to make a startling statement or to ask a thought-provoking question as the opening of your speech. Sometimes a really confident speaker may even use humor. Getting everyone to laugh is tricky, but if you can do it, it usually makes the listeners more receptive to what you are about to say.

If you were making a speech about summer jobs, the following might be a good opening statement: "You can be paid to avoid boredom." Most people's ears would perk up and you'd have their attention, at least for a few minutes. Once you had their attention, you'd proceed to explain the benefits of working during the summer and that two of those benefits were avoiding boredom and making money. Another attention-getter for the same topic might be the following: "Get the most from your summer break."

Here's your chance to write your own attention-getters. Write two opening statements for a speech about the benefits of having a summer job.

1. ____

____

2. ____

____

Now write two opening statements for a speech about the benefits of participating in team sports. Remember, you want to get the attention of your listeners.

1. ____

____

2. ____

____

Exchange with another student and critique each other's work. Keep your comments constructive!

Expert Tips

You can get some tips for public speaking by watching television. There are several types of broadcasts during which you can see and hear examples of public speaking. The types of broadcasts to look for include news programs, speeches made by political candidates and government officials, and interview shows.

Although some news shows, such as many of the "news magazines," are prerecorded, many news shows are recorded live. Watch the anchor carefully. Note his/her body language, eye contact, and facial expressions. Does he/she smile and remain serious at appropriate times?

You may have the opportunity to see and hear the President of the United States deliver a speech on television. Once a year the President delivers a State of the Union Address. In addition to prepared speeches, the President often holds press conferences. These conferences are situations in which a group of reporters have the opportunity to ask the President questions. The President's responses are not speeches, but they are a type of public speaking.

When an election is approaching, political candidates often appear on TV. They may be delivering speeches, debating opponents, or holding press conferences. (Paid political announcements are different.) Political candidates may be appearing in your area; perhaps you will be able to attend one of these events in person.

Although the situations described above may differ from what you may be asked to do, you can gain very valuable information by watching and analyzing these examples of public speaking. After all, many of these news anchors, reporters, public officials, and political candidates received many hours of training in public speaking before they reached their present positions.

Evaluate the Experts

Use this checklist to evaluate three expert speakers or the same speaker on three separate occasions. **You should have three copies of this sheet.**

Evaluation of ______________________________

Date: ____________________ By: ____________________

Reason for Speech: ______________________________

____

Where Seen: ______________________________

Rate the speaker according to the following system. Compare this person to other professional speakers you have heard. Fill in the appropriate numeral for each statement.

4: Excellent	**3: Very Good**	**2: Average**	**1: Not Very Good**

RATING

_____ 1. Has a good opening statement

_____ 2. Makes eye contact

_____ 3. Speaks clearly

_____ 4. Uses a good rate of speed

_____ 5. Speaks with expression

_____ 6. Appears comfortable

_____ 7. Uses appropriate facial expressions

_____ 8. Uses appropriate body language

_____ 9. Message sticks to the point and flows logically

_____ 10. Appears connected to the listeners (use of notes does not distract from speech)

OVERALL RATING: _______

WHAT I/HE/SHE DID WELL:

WHAT NEEDS MORE WORK:

Peer-/Self-Evaluation Checklist

Use copies of this checklist to evaluate the speeches given by you and your classmates.

Evaluation of ______________________________

Date: ______________ By: ______________________

Compare yourself and your peers to other non-professional speakers you have heard. Remember, the purpose of this activity is to help you and your classmates become better speakers; therefore, it is important to try to be honest and impartial as you fill out the forms. Rate the speeches according to the following system, filling in the appropriate numeral for each statement:

4: Excellent	**3: Very Good**	**2: Average**	**1: Not Very Good**

NOTE: To evaluate yourself, have someone videotape you delivering a two- to three-minute speech. Watch the videotape and try to be honest as you use the checklist to rate yourself. After your peers have rated you, you will probably want to compare your evaluation to theirs. You might see some interesting differences and similarities. If you feel that you did not do well in certain areas and are not sure how to improve, ask for suggestions.

RATING

_____ 1. Has a good opening statement

_____ 2. Makes eye contact

_____ 3. Speaks clearly

_____ 4. Uses a good rate of speed

_____ 5. Speaks with expression

_____ 6. Appears comfortable

_____ 7. Uses appropriate facial expressions

_____ 8. Uses appropriate body language

_____ 9. Message sticks to the point and flows logically

_____ 10. Appears connected to the listeners (use of notes does not distract from speech)

OVERALL RATING: _______

WHAT I/HE/SHE DID WELL:

WHAT NEEDS MORE WORK:

Framing Your Speech: The Main Parts of a Speech

Just as a house needs a framework to give it shape and to help it stand up, a good speech needs a framework to help keep it together, in sequence and on topic. The framework is basic and simple, but very effective. Every speech should have an introduction, a body (or middle), and a conclusion.

THE INTRODUCTION

The introduction is where you'll get the attention of the audience. It is where you will prepare the listeners for the full message of your speech. You want to get the listeners to focus on the issue that they are about to hear. State briefly what your speech is going to cover, including at least three main points.

THE BODY

The body is where you will give information and expand on the main points that you mentioned in the introduction. In the introduction you focused on a certain aspect of the topic. In the body you will expand that focus. You will repeat some information, but in much greater detail. Give examples, use statistics, and refer to visual displays. You might even want to use slides to emphasize and/or illustrate the points you are making.

THE CONCLUSION

The conclusion of your speech is where you will summarize your position and the points you made during the body of the speech. Draw together all of the information presented in the body. This is your opportunity to emphasize once more the points you presented in both the introduction and the body of the speech.

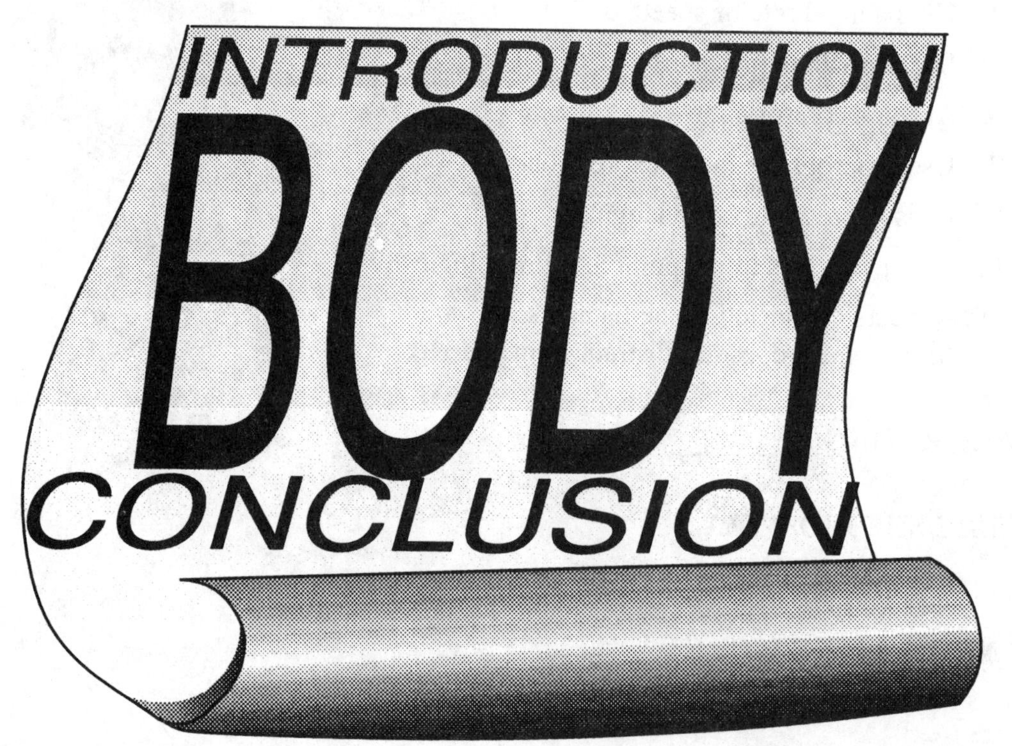

A Sample Speech

The following is a sample speech about summer jobs. Identify the **introduction**, the **body**, and the **conclusion**. Fill in the blanks accordingly.

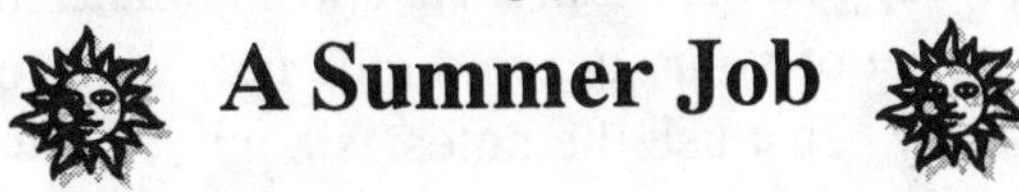

A Summer Job

____

Do you want to save yourself from boredom and save money at the same time? Get a summer job! While you are earning pocket money, you can also keep yourself from the horrors of boredom. Even a part-time job will allow you to earn spending money—maybe even money to save. What's more, you will be amazed at the many other benefits of a summer job!

____

There are many summer job opportunities available to students. Of course, certain jobs are more appropriate to certain age groups. Middle-school students may be able to get jobs as dog walkers, pet sitters, lawn caretakers, gardeners' helpers, recreation program counselors, mothers' helpers, or newspaper or flyer deliverers.

When you have a job during the summer months, you are given many opportunities to accomplish things. The most obvious one is the opportunity to make money. You are also given the opportunity to practice the handling of your own money. It is a perfect time to design a plan for spending and saving your earnings wisely. By doing this, you will show your parents that you are becoming responsible in new ways.

Your summer job may give you the opportunity to learn new skills. Depending on what the job is, you may have to learn something completely new or you may have to improve skills you already have. It is possible that you will learn to develop or refine habits, such as getting to your job on time, managing your time better, and doing your job to the best of your ability. You may experience a feeling of success at doing something that you did not think you could do or at learning something you did not think you could learn. A real sense of accomplishment will be yours.

Another aspect of your summer job is the chance it gives you to meet new people. You also have a chance to interact with people in a different way than you might at school. You may not be aware that it is happening, but you will be learning valuable skills that you will use later in your life.

Frequently, by getting and keeping a summer job, students discover that their parents and other adults have a new respect and admiration for them. This part-time summer job may also pave the way for other opportunities.

Of course, another benefit of getting a summer job is that you will not be bored. You will be able to fill your time constructively and still have time to have fun with your friends.

____

As you can see, there are many benefits to getting and keeping a part-time summer job. Let me mention them again: earning your own money, showing that you can be responsible for handling money, learning new skills, learning things about yourself, meeting new people, interacting with others in a non-school setting, earning respect of adults, and avoiding boredom. Regardless of how many of these things occur because of your summer job, it will still be a valuable experience in more ways than one.

Using Note Cards

One way to organize a speech is to list important words or facts on note cards. Opening words, important details that support the main idea, and summarizing statements can be noted. However, do not write too much of your speech on the note cards or you might be tempted to read rather than to speak freely. Just use the notes as a guide. Always remember to focus on your audience when you are giving a speech! It might be helpful to list your key thoughts in outline form. An example follows:

My First Airplane Flight

I. Ride to airport
II. Almost missed plane
III. Friendly pilot
IV. Watched movie
V. Happy landing

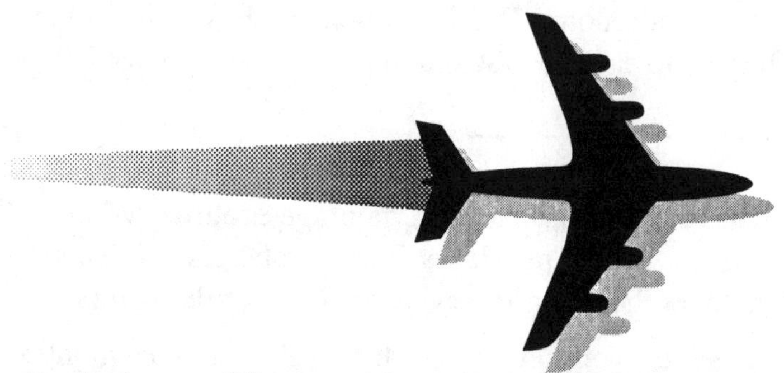

Pretend that you are about to give a speech about a "first experience." Fill in the note card below. What key ideas would you list that would help you to remember your speech?

Using an Outline

Some speakers prefer to use an outline instead of note cards. Outlining is another way to organize information and your thoughts; it can help you stay focused as you gather information. It will also help you keep your remarks flowing and in logical order when you write your speech. As with note cards, you must remember not to read from your outline. Rather, you should glance at your outline from time to time to keep yourself on target.

Outlines divide the subject into several parts:

Title: The title tells what the outline is all about.

Main Topic: Each main topic tells a very important idea. It is numbered with a Roman numeral and a period.

Subtopic: Each subtopic gives some information about the main topic. A capital letter followed by a period is used for each.

Details: Details give extra information relating to the topic. Cardinal numbers followed by a period are used. If more detailed information is needed, lower case letters followed by a period are used.

Weave the parts of your outline into the appropriate parts of your speech. Keep in mind all that you learned about framing your speech. Remember to write a good opening sentence in order to get the listeners' attention. Look at the sample outline below.

LEARNING TO SWIM

I. Reasons for learning
  A. Enjoyment
    1. In warm weather
    2. All year
  B. Team sport
  C. Survival
    1. My own
    2. Helping others
II. Where to get lessons
  A. Swim club
  B. Sports center
  C. Community center
  D. School
  E. Neighborhood pool

Pretend that you are going to give a speech about learning to do something. Write an outline for that speech on another sheet of paper.

Just Before Speaking...

You may not know it, but many performers and athletes have a mental and physical routine that they go through just before they perform. Their routines may be talking to themselves, going through the motions of the physical activity, imagining themselves performing it perfectly, meditating, doing relaxation exercises, or calling a certain person on the phone.

It may help you to feel confident and prepared if shortly before your speech, you check yourself according to the following items. You may want to add things to this list to personalize it to meet your own needs.

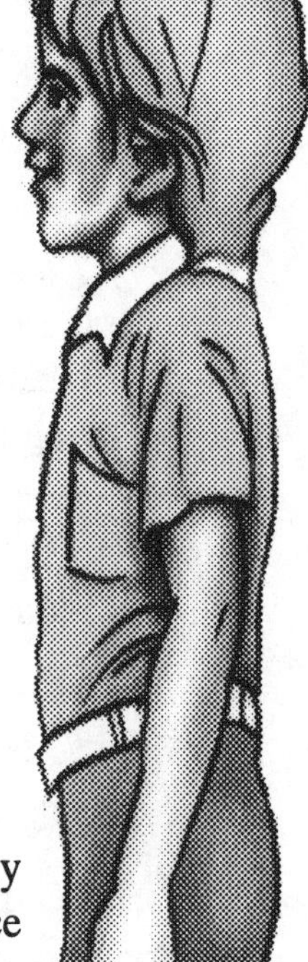

1. Check your appearance in a mirror, a full-length one if you have it. Is your hair neat? Is your shirt tucked in? Do you feel generally presentable and comfortable in your clothing?
2. If you are using an outline, review it.
3. If you are using note cards, make sure that they are easy to read and in the correct order.
4. Remind yourself that you are a good speaker and that you have prepared yourself well. There is NO reason to expect a problem!
5. Don't be afraid if you are nervous. Most speakers feel nervous. Just take a deep breath; it helps you get more oxygen to your brain, which aids in thinking. Taking a deep breath also helps to relax you. (You can also do this during your speaking presentation.)
6. If you forget a word or phrase, don't freeze up trying to think of it. Simply substitute another word or phrase that means the same thing. The audience will not know that you've made a change.
7. It will help to remember that everyone else would feel the same in your situation.
8. Remind yourself that everyone wants you to do well.

Pick a Prompt: Topics for Speaking

The prompt topics on the next page will be reproduced, cut apart, and placed in a large envelope, box, or other container.

RULES

1. Students will take turns picking one of the prompts from the container. (If necessary, include duplicates of some of the prompts.)

2. Each student will be given fifteen minutes to prepare a short speech on the chosen topic.

3. Students should remember to use the basic elements of good speaking discussed in this section of the book.

4. Students will listen politely to the speeches of the other students.

5. After each speech, students will use the Peer-/Self-Evaluation Checklist to rate the speech and to offer suggestions for improvement.

Pick a Prompt: Topics for Speaking

A KEY PERSON IN MY LIFE	A PERFECT DAY
A STORYBOOK CHARACTER I'D LIKE TO MEET	SOME RAINY-DAY FUN
A PLACE I'D LIKE TO VISIT	A JOB I DID NOT LIKE
MY SPECIAL HOBBY	A GREAT PET TO OWN
A TV SHOW WORTH VIEWING	MY DREAM HOUSE
MY FAVORITE FOOD	ME IN 2033
HOW TO EARN AN "A" IN SCHOOL	TWO SPORTS I ENJOY
THE MESSIEST ROOM IN MY HOUSE	HOW TO STAY HEALTHY
THE MOST IMPORTANT INVENTION	AN AGE I'D LIKE TO BE
A HERO IN HISTORY	A SPECIAL ACHIEVEMENT

SECTION II

Putting It into Practice

Choral Speaking: Famous Poetry

Choral speaking, or speaking in unison, is fun to do. Narrative poems like "Paul Revere's Ride" and "Hiawatha's Childhood," both written by Henry Wadsworth Longfellow, are good poems to use for choral recitations. Another good choice for choral reading is "Casey at the Bat," written by Ernest Thayer.

Divide the poems into speaking sections, or parts. For example, you might mark one verse "Girls' Part" and another verse "Boys' Part." Rows or sections of the classroom can also be used as speaking divisions. Solo parts can be included to vary the choral presentation.

On this page and the next are excerpts from two of the poems mentioned above. You may use one or both of these, or you may find your own narrative poems for your choral speaking project. Be sure to vary your tone of voice when you are reciting a poem!

Paul Revere's Ride

by Henry Wadsworth Longfellow

Listen my children and you shall hear
Of the midnight ride of Paul Revere,
On the eighteenth of April, in Seventy-five;
Hardly a man is now alive
Who remembers that famous day and year.

He said to his friend, "If the British march
By land or sea from the town tonight,
Hang a lantern aloft in the the belfry arch
Of the North Church tower as a signal light—
One if by land, and two if by sea;
And I on the opposite shore will be,
Ready to ride and spread the alarm
Through every Middlesex village and farm,
For the country folk to be up and to arm."

Then he said "Good-night!" and with muffled oar
Silently rowed to the Charlestown shore,
Just as the moon rose over the bay
Where swinging wide at her moorings lay
The *Somerset,* British man-of-war;
A phantom ship, with each mast and spar
Across a huge black hulk, that was magnified
By its own reflection in the tide.

Hiawatha's Childhood

by Henry Wadsworth Longfellow

By the shores of Gitche Gumee,
By the shining Big-Sea-Water
Stood the wigwam of Nokomis,
Daughter of the Moon, Nokomis.
Dark behind it rose the forest,
Rose the black and gloomy pine-trees,
Rose the firs with cones upon them;
Bright before it beat the water,
Beat the clear and sunny water.
Beat the shining Big-Sea-Water.

There the wrinkled old Nokomis
Nursed the little Hiawatha,
Rocked him in his linden cradle,
Bedded soft in moss and rushes,
Safely bound with reindeer sinews;
Stilled his fretful wail by saying,
"Hush, the Naked Bear will hear thee!"
Lulled him into slumber, singing,
"Ewa-yea! my little owlet!
Who is this, that lights the wigwam?
With his great eyes light the wigwam?
Ewa-yea! my little owlet!"

Choral Speaking: Famous Speeches

Students often enjoy using famous speeches in choral speaking presentations. With your group, choose a favorite speech and read it carefully. Make copies of the speech and distribute them to each group member. Underline words, phrases, and sentences that will require special emphasis when they are recited.

Divide the speech into parts and label the names of the speakers on each part. Students may memorize the speaking parts or they may read them. Practice the speech together before performing it in front of an assembly of other classes. The following are parts of two famous speeches to help you get started.

★★★ JOHN F. KENNEDY'S INAUGURAL ADDRESS (1961) ★★★

And so, my fellow Americans: ask not what your country can do for you—ask what you can do for your country.

My fellow citizens of the world: ask not what America will do for you, but what together we can do for the freedom of man.

Finally, whether you are citizens of America or citizens of the world, ask of us here the same high standards of strength and sacrifice which we ask of you. With a good conscience our only sure reward, with history the final judge of our deeds, let us go forth to lead the land we love, asking His blessing and His help, but knowing that here on earth God's work must truly be our own.

★★★ ABRAHAM LINCOLN'S GETTYSBURG ADDRESS (1863) ★★★

Four score and seven years ago our fathers brought forth on this continent a new nation, conceived in liberty and dedicated to the proposition that all men are created equal.

Now we are engaged in a great civil war, testing whether that nation or any nation so conceived and so dedicated can long endure. We are met on a great battlefield of that war. We have come to dedicate a portion of that field as a final resting-place for those who here gave their lives that that nation might live. It is altogether fitting and proper that we should do this.

But in a larger sense, we cannot dedicate, we cannot consecrate, we cannot hallow this ground. The brave men, living and dead who struggled here have consecrated it far above our poor power to add or detract. The world will little note nor long remember what we say here, but it can never forget what they did here. It is for us the living rather to be dedicated here to the unfinished work which they who fought here have thus far so nobly advanced. It is rather for us to be here dedicated to the great task remaining before us—that from these honored dead we take increased devotion to that cause for which they gave the last full measure of devotion—that we here highly resolve that these dead shall not have died in vain, that this nation under God shall have a new birth of freedom, and that government of the people, by the people, for the people shall not perish from the earth.

Creative Dramatics

In this activity, you will take part in a speaking activity with a partner. Choose a classmate to work with you in developing a creative dramatics presentation based upon the scenarios that are listed below. Read them carefully. Then select one of them to dramatize. Each presentation should last approximately three minutes. Both partners should contribute to the dialogue equally.

Remember the rules of good public speaking. Speak clearly and add emotion when needed. Use the correct body language. If you have time, it is a good idea to rehearse your act before presenting it to the class.

SCENARIOS

1. COACH AND PLAYER: Team is losing the game
2. TEACHER AND STUDENT: Homework seems to be lost
3. PARENT AND CHILD: Parent is too overprotective
4. BABY SITTER AND CHILD: Child will not go to sleep
5. FATHER AND SON: Son damages family's new car
6. TWO STUDENTS: They repair a broken friendship
7. POLICE OFFICER AND WITNESS: They try to recall details of a crime
8. PRINCIPAL AND STUDENT: They discuss an incident on the playground
9. TWO YOUNG CHILDREN: They are running away from home
10. REPORTER AND STAR: TV interview

Speech Planning Form

Like most things you wish to accomplish, a good speech requires a plan. The following outline will help you plan your speech. You may change or omit parts of the form to personalize it to meet your own needs.

TOPIC: ______________________________

INTRODUCTION

Attention-Getter

____

____

Three or More Main Points

____

____

____

____

BODY: Examples and Additional Information

____

____

____

____

CONCLUSION: Summary of Your Position and Your Main Points

____

____

VISUAL AIDS: Slides, Posters, Charts, Etc.

____

____

SOURCES OF INFORMATION

____

____

All About Me!

Here is an opportunity for the students in your class to get to know each other better and to practice oral communication. Fill in the chart below. Then write the information on note cards. Underline or highlight the key words. Use the note cards when you present your oral autobiography to the class.

AUTOBIOGRAPHICAL TOPICS

NAME: ______________________________

DATE OF BIRTH: ______________________________

PLACE OF BIRTH: ______________________________

Autobiography

FAMILY INFORMATION:

____

____

____

FAVORITE HOBBIES AND/OR SPORTS:

____

____

____

FUN VACATIONS:

____

____

BEST FRIENDS:

____

____

SCHOOL LIKES AND DISLIKES:

____

____

FUTURE PLANS:

____

____

Follow the rules for good public speaking found in The First Steps Section of this book. Don't be nervous. Remember, you know your subject better than anyone else.

Sharing Your Own Experiences

Think of special times or experiences in your life that were particularly noteworthy. Review your list of experiences. Choose one of those experiences for a speech. Organize your thoughts about it into a logical sequence.

- When and where did the experience take place?
- Who were the people involved?
- What happened first, second, third, and so on?
- Why was this experience so memorable?

It is important to get your audience quickly involved in what you are saying, so plan a good opening sentence. (EXAMPLE: Preparing for the unexpected was a lesson I learned the hard way during my camping trip out west.) Good ending sentences are important too. (EXAMPLE: From that time on, the boys never underestimated the girls' ability in sports.)

Write your talk about your experiences in the space below. Be sure to use correct grammar. Practice your speech with a classmate before presenting it to the whole class. Include the examples for improving speech that were discussed in Section I: The First Steps. Underline important words in your speech that you want to emphasize. You might want to prepare visual aids to support your speech. Give your speech a title.

____

____

____

____

____

____

____

____

____

____

____

____

____

____

Oral Description

In this activity, you are asked to create an oral word picture of a favorite or familiar place. Select a location and make a list of details. Use your senses of seeing, hearing, feeling, tasting, and smelling to recall details associated with the place.

EXAMPLE: Baseball Stadium

Roar of the Crowd—Hearing
Players on the Field—Seeing
Popcorn and Hot Dogs—Tasting and Smelling
Hot Sun Beating Down—Feeling

MY LOCATION: ______________________

DETAILS:

____

____

____

____

____

____

____

After you have listed details that describe your location, organize them into a short and logically sequenced oral presentation. You will need to add a good opening and closing sentence. For example, "Sparkling lakes and gentle breezes await you here."

You may choose to make your presentation into a "Mystery Place." If so, do not give the location before you speak. Instead, allow your classmates to listen to your word picture clues carefully and guess the place you are describing.

Remember, when you give an oral presentation, it is important to vary the volume of your voice and to speak clearly and confidently.

Sparkling lakes and gentle breezes await you here.

On the Air: School Newscasters

A school radio or television news program is a great experience for public speaking. If neither is available in your school, perhaps your school intercom system can be used. If none of these systems is available, create a studio in your classroom. Everyone can take a turn being the news anchor, sportscaster, and weather person.

Using video, radio, or the intercom system may allow you to be more relaxed than when you give a speech in front of a large gathering. Also, you can sit and relax physically. Another advantage of a radio or intercom news program is that you can rely on notes more extensively than when giving a live speech. Even television reporting allows you to use notes more freely than in a live speech, for you can use prompts that are not seen by the audience.

Decide if you will report on school news, sports, weather, special events, or an issue of concern. Write your report. Practice it and have it timed. Remember to speak clearly, pronouncing each syllable. Use proper inflection for questions, statements, excitement, and wonder.

TYPE: ______________________________

TOPIC: ____

Write your report in the space below.

Let's Debate

Debates are formal arguments *for* or *against* a given statement or topic. They offer a wonderful opportunity to practice good public speaking. For this activity you will divide into debating teams. You will then be given an issue to debate. Decide which side of the issue you will represent and develop evidence to support your side of the argument. You must also prepare a *rebuttal* speech in order to answer the attacks and evidence that the other team might present.

You may want to record your facts on note cards to use during the debate; however, it is not effective to read the notes while debating. The team that presents the most logical and convincing argument wins the debate.

DEBATING TOPICS: Choose one of these or another approved by your teacher.

SCHOOLS SHOULD BE OPEN ALL YEAR ROUND.

PARENTS SHOULD CENSOR WHAT THEIR CHILDREN WATCH ON TV.

STUDENTS MUST MAINTAIN A HIGH GRADE AVERAGE IN ORDER TO QUALIFY FOR EXTRA CURRICULAR ACTIVIITES.

MY DEBATING TOPIC:

____

MY TEAM'S POSITION ON THE ISSUE (FOR OR AGAINST): ____________

Gather facts on this page. Your constructive speech in which you present your argument and your rebuttal speech will be written on other sheets of paper. Use library reference materials, computer research, or interviews to obtain information to support your position.

____

____

____

____

____

____

____

____

____

____

Making Introductions

For this activity you will have to do some role playing! You will practice your public-speaking skills by making introductions and by being introduced in different circumstances. Before you begin, try to recall introductions you've heard on television or in real life. When two persons are introduced by a third, certain guidelines should be followed. For example, you should introduce the elder of the two persons, remembering to use the person's title: Dr., Mrs., Mr., etc.

I'D LIKE TO INTRODUCE...

With your classmates, role play the following situations requiring introductions. First think about each situation and write notes on what you might say in each case. Take turns introducing and being introduced.

1. Your parent and a friend
2. Your parent and your friend's parent
3. Your grandparent and a teacher
4. Your coach (any sport) and your father
5. Your old friend and your new friend

PRESENTING...

Now imagine that these people are going to address an assembly in your school. You are in charge of introducing one or more of them to the audience.

1. The lead singer of an extremely popular band or singing group
2. The author of a best-selling book, one that is a hit with everyone at school
3. A NASCAR driver who once attended your school
4. A host of a popular music video television show
5. A player from a champion professional sports team
6. An individual who has just completed a major accomplishment, such as climbing Mt. Everest or sailing around the world solo

Choose one of the people listed above and write a speech in which you introduce that person to the audience. Use note cards or an outline to help you prepare for the presentation of your speech. Review the basic elements of good public speaking presented in the first section of this book. Present your speech to your classmates.

Old Time Radio Shows

In the years before television became such an important part of our lives, people depended on the radio for news and entertainment. Many types of radio shows—comedies, mysteries, dramas, and adventures—were popular with listeners. In this activity, you are asked to work with a small group of students to create a radio show and to tape record it using sound effects.

If possible, try to obtain a tape of an old-time radio show before starting the project. Some memorable shows include *Inner Sanctum, The Lone Ranger, The Green Hornet, Amos and Andy,* and *Fibber McGee and Molly.* Because actors could not be seen, they did not wear costumes or make-up. They stood in front of microphones and read their scripts, usually in front of live audiences. Sound effects, such as footsteps, galloping horses, or stormy weather, were created in the radio studio.

Meet with your group and brainstorm ideas for radio scripts. Decide on a title and characters. As you write your script, note the places where sound effects should be used. Make sure that each group member will have a speaking part and a chance to create a sound effect. Rehearse your script several times before tape recording it. Some group members may disguise their voices and take more than one role. On Old Time Radio Day in class, each group will present its show by playing the tape for the class.

Write your radio script in the space below.

____
title

Ad Campaign Presentation

Divide into "ad agency" groups of four or five students. Each agency will have the job of designing an ad campaign for a new breakfast food. The groups will do the following:

- Create and name the breakfast food.
- Create a slogan for the product.
- Produce a TV commercial to promote it.

Paper, cardboard, crayons, paint, and other arts-and-crafts supplies should be provided for this activity.

PART I: A NEW BREAKFAST FOOD
As a group, brainstorm ideas for a new breakfast food. Write the responses below. Then choose the best idea and give your new breakfast food a name.

____

____

____

____

____

Our breakfast food is called ______________________________.

PART II: A SLOGAN
As a group, brainstorm ideas for a slogan to advertise your new breakfast food. Write the responses below. Then choose the best idea.

____

____

____

____

OUR SLOGAN: ________________________________

____

PART III: CREATE A TV COMMERCIAL
As a group, write a TV commerical using script form. Each member of the agency should play a role in the commercial. Use the following sheet to help you.

Ad Campaign Presentation: Create a TV Commercial

Create a TV commercial to promote your new breakfast food product. As a group, write your commercial using script form. Each member of the agency should play a role in the commercial. Use *propaganda* methods to convince others to buy your product.

EXAMPLES OF PROPAGANDA:

NUMBERS: We're number one in sales! We've been in business for 15 years.

BANDWAGON: All the kids in the neighborhood are eating this delicious food. I want some too.

DEGREES AND TITLES: Nutritionists and doctors agree that this food is healthy for us.

Write your TV commercial script in the space below. Rehearse it with your group until all members have memorized their parts. During a special time set aside by the teacher, each ad agency group will present its ad campaign. Props, costumes, and scenery can be created to use in the performance. The teacher or another faculty member can act as a judge and evaluate the ad campaigns.

____

____

____

____

____

____

____

____

____

____

____

____

____

____

Photo Fun

Photographs help us to recall memorable times in our lives. For this activity, locate one favorite photograph to use in an oral presentation to the class.

Birthday parties, special vacations, school activities, or family fun are all good photo choices. In your oral presentation, you will tell the story of what is happening in the photo.

Describe the photo you plan to use.

Plan your photo talk. Use the note-card method described in The First Steps Section of this book. Write down key ideas or words that will help you remember your thoughts in logical order.

A Day in the Life of a Community Helper

Think about the people who work in your community. There are many who contribute greatly to the well-being of the citizens. Make a list of community helpers. Try to think of many different people. The list has been started for you.

mayor
police officer

Select one of the community helpers on your list to research. If possible, include a personal interview with that person. Think about the following questions: What are the positive and negative aspects of the job? How is the community helped by this person's efforts? Write your notes in the space below.

After you have obtained information, use the facts to prepare a speech about a day in the life of this community helper. Your speech should be approximately four minutes long. Follow the suggestions for improving public speaking discussed in Section I: The First Steps. Obtain props or other visual aids to enhance your presentation. On the day of your presentation, you might want to dress up like the community helper you are describing!

A Day in the Life of ...

____

____

____

____

____

____

____

____

Teacher for a Day

Would you like to be teacher for a day? What type of lesson would you teach the class? To help you prepare for your first teaching effort, fill in the form below.

1. The subject I will teach is ______________________________.
2. The main object of my lesson (what I hope to accomplish) is the following:

   ____

   ____

3. I will need the following materials for my lesson (books, computer software, worksheets, etc.):

   ____

   ____

4. I hope to cover the following ideas or topics:

   ____

   ____

TEACHING TIPS

Learn the material that you will be teaching to others.

Ask your teacher for advice in planning the lesson.

Create a lesson plan that is creative and challenging.

Make sure each student is following the lesson while you are teaching.

Speak clearly and slowly when relating information.

Vary your speaking voice to add interest and excitement.

Evaluate the students' comprehension of the lesson.

Story Villains Speak Out

We're often told that there are two sides to every story; however, we rarely get to hear a tale told from the story villain's point of view. In this unique speaking activity, wicked characters, such as the Big Bad Wolf or Captain Hook, will finally have a chance to relate their impressions of what really happened!

Think of a story villain who "deserves" to have his or her side of the story communicated fairly. In the space below, write this character's account of the plot events. Use the first-person point of view (I, we, my, our, etc.). After you have completed your writing, read it carefully. Underline the words that need to be emphasized. Note the phrases of sentences that need to be spoken quickly or slowly for special dramatic effect. Practice your talk using clear diction. Pretend that you really are this character! Try to evoke sympathy for your character's plight.

On the day that you present your story villain's tale to your classmates, you may want to dress up as the character to enhance your oral presentation.

CHARACTER'S NAME: ______________________________

TITLE OF STORY: ______________________________

MY SIDE OF THE STORY

How to Conduct a Meeting

The officers of the Rockview Middle School Student Council conducted a meeting last week. They followed a set of rules for conducting meetings that is called parliamentary procedure. Lori Stephens, the president, was in charge of the meeting. Ki Su Yung, the secretary, took notes of the proceedings. These notes are called minutes. Bob Carson, the vice-president, made a motion, or suggestion, to end the meeting. Carol Peters has seconded the motion according to the proper order of the meeting.

With a small group of your classmates, imagine that you are all part of a club or group at school that is holding a meeting. Create roles for each group member. Look up the complete rules of parliamentary procedure and use them in your skit. Write your meeting skit in the space below. Present it to the class at a given time. Evaluate each group's efforts.

The Meeting of the ________________________ Club

CLUB MEETING TONIGHT!

CLUB HOUSE

Persuasive Speaking

Your job is to convince your audience that your ideas are important and should be considered and evaluated carefully. In order to do that, your speech should contain supporting evidence to back up your conclusions on a particular subject. For example, suppose you think that your school should hold an annual dance for middle-grade students. Your supporting statements might include the following: Students will act responsibly. They will decorate the gym, serve refreshments, provide music, and clean up after the dance. Always be positive in your presentation. Be clear and logical in the way you present your facts. Have a strong ending sentence.

Choose a topic to use with your classmates. It can relate to a school or a community situation. It should last approximately three minutes. Use the note-card method of preparation. Write your speech in the space below.

Persuasive Topic

"How-to" Talks

In this activity you will put your public-speaking skills into practice by speaking about **how to** do or make something. First you must decide what is to be done or made. It should be something that you have successfully done yourself. Choose something that you feel comfortable explaining to others. Next think of the logical steps to follow which will result in the successful completion of the project. Write your speech, incorporating these directions. You may wish to have the finished project on hand or in varying stages of completion. Remember to begin your speech with an attention-getting sentence.

EXAMPLE:

HOW TO MAKE A PEANUT BUTTER AND JELLY SANDWICH

1. Assemble the ingredients: 2 slices of bread, peanut butter, and jelly or jam.
2. Get a plate and a spreading knife.
3. Put the bread on the plate.
4. Spread the peanut butter to cover one side of one slice of bread.
5. Spread the jelly or jam to cover one side of the other slice of bread.
6. Put the two slices of bread together so that the spread sides are on the inside.
7. If desired, cut the sandwich into halves (rectangular or triangular) or quarters (square or triangular).
8. Clean up any mess and put away the ingredients.
9. Enjoy!

HOW TO ______________________________

1. ______________________________
2. ______________________________
3. ______________________________
4. ______________________________
5. ______________________________
6. ______________________________
7. ______________________________
8. ______________________________

Giving Directions to a Location

Knowing how to give and follow directions to a specific location are important skills that are often used in daily life. Here are a few tips to remember:

- ☞ Keep the directions simple.
- ☞ Speak clearly.
- ☞ Give the directions in logical order.
- ☞ Use words like "first," "second," "next," and "last" to help define the correct order.
- ☞ Picture the directions in your mind before you give them orally.
- ☞ Add special details, such as landmarks, to help locate destinations.

Work with a partner and take turns giving oral directions to a place in your school or your community. A few suggestions are listed below:

- ❃ Walk from your classroom to the school office.
- ❃ Walk from your classroom to the lunchroom.
- ❃ Walk from your classroom to the nurse's office.
- ❃ Walk from the gym to the art room.
- ❃ Walk from the music room to the front door of the school building.
- ❃ Walk from your home to the school.
- ❃ Walk from the school to a friend's home.

Were your directions clear and complete? If not, how can you improve them?

____

____

____

____

____

____

Television Review

Now is your chance to watch television as a legitimate school assignment! For this activity, you will be a TV critic and will give a two- to three-minute oral report about a television show. Pay attention to the broadcast and take notes as you watch.

Think about your favorite shows. List five of those shows in the space below.

1. ______________________________
2. ______________________________
3. ______________________________
4. ______________________________
5. ______________________________

Put a √ next to your favorite show. You teacher must approve your choice of show.

Fill in the following form to help you organize the information about the TV show you review.

TV SHOW: ______________________________

Type of Show: (Situation Comedy, Drama, Documentary, Series, Special, Other): ______

____

Date and Time Show Was Aired: ______________________________

Theme: ______________________________

____

____

Opinion of Script: ______________________________

____

____

Opinion of Acting: ______________________________

____

____

Believability of the Plot: ______________________________

____

____

Overall Rating and Recommendation: ______________________________

____

____

Just for Fun!

In this activity you are asked to speak about fun! Think of something that is fun to **do.** Explain what this activity is and why this represents fun for you. Is it something done as an individual or with a group? Is this something that others would also enjoy doing? How did you come to enjoy it? What are the skills involved? What equipment is needed? Make notes to help guide you through your two- to three-minute speech. An example of the notes follows:

ICE SKATING:
Can be done alone or with friends.
Can make new friends.
Skates, warm clothing, and pond for outdoors.
Skates and rink for indoors.
Balance and other athletic skills developed.
Confidence builder.
Why I came to enjoy it:
None of my brothers or sisters enjoy it.
Gives me freedom to be me.
I'm not as big or as bright, but I can do something they can't.

I think ________________________________ **is fun to do.**

DETAILS:

____

____

____

____

____

____

____

____

____

____

After you have written your topic and some of the details, arrange them in a short, logically sequenced talk. Remember to add an attention-getting sentence at the beginning. You will also need a good finishing sentence.

Storytelling

For this activity you will choose a story and read it aloud to the class. Select a story that you have enjoyed reading and that is appropriate to tell in class. A tale with interesting characters and dialogue and an exciting, fast-paced plot would be a good choice. Tall tales and myths are always fun to tell aloud. Avoid choosing a story that is too long or too complicated.

HELPFUL HINTS

Be dramatic. Vary your voice to represent the spoken language of different characters in the story.

Emphasize key words. If possible, use a tape recorder to evaluate your storytelling.

Be sure to use the correct gestures and body language to enhance your presentation.

Memorize the story and practice telling it several times at home before telling it to the class.

CHOOSING A STORY

Think of the many stories you have read. List six stories that would be suitable to read to your class. Next to each, list one or more characters and the emotion that is needed to portray each character correctly. For example, in the myth "Echo and Narcissus," Zeus is angry and Echo is bewildered.

STORY TITLE	CHARACTER(S)	EMOTION
____________	____________	____________
____________	____________	____________
____________	____________	____________
____________	____________	____________
____________	____________	____________
____________	____________	____________

The story I have chosen to tell is ______________________________

An Election Campaign Speech

In this activity you must imagine that you are campaigning for an elected position. It may be for a school office or it may be for a club to which you belong. Think about why you are the best qualified candidate. Of course, you need to know something about the responsibilities of the position. You may also want to learn what past officers have or have not done while in office.

As part of the campaign, you will need to address groups to convey to them that you are the best choice for the position. Prepare a two-minute speech explaining the reasons why you should be elected to represent them.

Complete the following form to get started with your campaign speech. Remember to use a good opening statement, to construct your speech in logical order, and to have a strong ending sentence. Speak clearly, confidently, and expressively.

I will be a candidate for (office and organization): ______________________________

Responsibilities of the office:

____

____

Why I am the best qualified:

____

____

How I will improve the organization:

____

____

★ THE ★
★★CANDIDATES★★
★★★SPEAK★★★

Celebrity Interview

For this cooperative-learning activity, you will choose a famous person you would like to pretend to be. (You must get this person approved by your teacher before you begin this activity.) You should know some information about this person. Pretending to be this celebrity, you will be interviewed by a classmate. When you answer the interviewer's questions, answer as you think your chosen celebrity would answer.

Things to remember when conducting these interviews:

1. Each student will choose a famous personality to pretend to be.
2. The teacher must approve that celebrity.
3. Students will be assigned to interview each other.
4. Both the interviewer and the interviewee should do some research on the celebrity. You will want to ask and answer questions intelligently.
5. The teacher will determine the schedule for conducting the interviews in class.

Use the following form to prepare the questions you will ask as interviewer:

INTERVIEW OF ______________________________

PORTRAYED BY ______________________________

INTERVIEWED BY ______________________________

QUESTIONS:

____

____

____

____

____

____

____

____

____

____

____

A Classroom Museum

In this exercise you will pretend that your classroom is a gallery in an art museum. Choose a favorite drawing, poster, framed reproduction, or original piece of art to display. Other choices might include pottery, decorative glass, woven art, or statuary.

As a "museum guide," be prepared to give an explanation of the particular piece of art you have included in the display. Your classmates will be the museum visitors. Complete the form below to help you compose your presentation.

NAME OF THE WORK: ______________________________

TYPE OF WORK: ______________________________

DESCRIPTION OF WORK: (Include an explanation of symbolism, etc.)

____

____

____

____

ESTIMATED CURRENT VALUE OF WORK: ______________________________

BIOGRAPHICAL INFORMATION ABOUT THE ARTIST:

Artist's Birth Date and Nationality: ______________________________

Interesting Facts about Artist's Life:

____

____

____

____

Training and Recognition:

____

____

The artist is mainly known for ______________________________

____

____

____

Personal Treasures

We all have possessions which we care about very much. Often these objects are not valuable in the monetary sense. We have other reasons for attaching importance and value to these things.

Think of something you treasure. Why do you feel this way? Write a short speech in which you share your feelings with your class. You may want to bring the object to class. Use the following outline to help you organize your thoughts.

OBJECT: ______________________________

MONETARY VALUE: __________

This object is important to me because ______________________________

____

____

____

____

Write your speech in the space below. Use the form introduced in Section I: **Introduction** (with your attention-getter), **Body** (with at least three main points), and **Conclusion** (where you summarize your main points).

____

____

____

____

____

____

____

____

____

____

____

Current Events

For this activity you are asked to speak about a current event. To most people, this usually means something that is noteworthy for one reason or another and has been reported in the news. Your teacher may ask that the event be of a certain category.

To get started, scan the newspaper or watch the television news. Choose a current event that interests you. Follow the event for three days. Collect news clippings or take notes from the television coverage. Be prepared to share with your classmates what you have learned about this "history-in-the-making" event. Your presentation should last at least two minutes. There may be things that you want to use in your presentation, such as a wall map, a globe, posters, slides, or a videotape. Remember to follow the guidelines discussed in Section I.

The current event I will discuss is ________________________________

____

____

____

____

I am interested in this event because ______________________________

____

____

I think that others need to know about this event because ______________

____

____

I will use the following audio-visual aids in my presentation: __________

____

____

A Special Someone

Each of us could probably list several persons whom we admire. There may be different reasons for our admiration of each of them. Think of a person whom you admire. You may want to consider parents, grandparents, and other relatives; teachers and coaches; community leaders; members of the clergy; and political leaders.

Pretend that you are nominating this person for an award. Suppose the award is entitled "The Greatest Person I Know." As part of the nomination, you are responsible for explaining the reasons why this person is worthy of this title and recognition. Pay tribute to this person in a short speech. In your speech, explain the individual's qualities and accomplishments that you believe are remarkable and admirable.

I admire ____

____

____

____

Prepare note cards or an outline before your write your speech. Try to have a large photograph or a collage of photographs of this person to show to your audience when you make this tribute speech.

Cause and Effect

One action may bring about another. This is known as cause and effect. Identifying the cause and the effect is an important critical-thinking skill. In this public-speaking activity you are asked to speak about a cause-and-effect relationship for two to three minutes. Create a list cause/effect relationships. The list has been started for you. Choose one of the topics from the list to be the subject of your speech.

Cause and Effect Relationships

1. Forest Destruction and Global Warming
2. Advertising and Teen/Youth Tobacco Use
3. Breaking a Household Rule and Losing Privileges

5. ______________________________

6. ______________________________

7. ______________________________

8. ______________________________

Choose one of the above topics and write your speech in the space below.

____

____

____

____

____

____

____

____

____

____

____

____

____

SECTION III

All Around Town

Choosing a Site

In this culminating activity, All Around Town, you and your classmates will become tour guides and present oral speeches about special places in your community. Use this page to help you select sites for your presentations.

I. With your classmates, brainstorm a list of interesting or unusual places in your town. Think of municipal buildings, commercial establishments, recreational sites, religious structures, and buildings that are architecturally unique. List the sites in the column on the left.

II. Each student will select a different site to research for an oral presentation. (One student should be selected to serve as announcer for the presentation.)

COMMUNITY SITE	STUDENT
ANNOUNCER	

Gathering Information

This page will help you to gather and organize facts about your selected site. Consult with librarians, teachers, neighbors and other residents, and/or government officials to learn more about your community site. Reference materials may be available to help you also. After you have gathered facts and written them on this page, use the information to develop your tour guide speech. Try to obtain photos, pictures, slides and other visual materials to use in your oral presentation.

COMMUNITY SITE: ______________________________

LOCATION: ______________________________

TYPE OF STRUCTURE (Examples: stadium, school, museum): ______________

AGE OF STRUCTURE: ______________________________

MATERIALS USED TO BUILD STRUCTURE: ______________________________

____

____

ARCHITECT: ______________________________

IMPORTANCE OF SITE TO COMMUNITY: ______________________________

____

____

____

____

____

ADDITIONAL INFORMATION: ______________________________

____

____

____

____

____

____

____

Planning Your Speech

PART I: ORGANIZE YOUR INFORMATION

You have selected a community site and have collected information about it. Now you must organize this information into a tour guide speech for the All Around Town oral presentation. In order to make your talk as creative and interesting as possible, prepare or gather visual aids to accompany your words. For example, a map to show the location of the site would be very helpful. Slides, photos, or sketches of the site could also be included. You might even construct a model or diorama scene to show the audience more detail about your special site. List your ideas below.

Ideas for Visual Aids:

____

____

____

As you write your speech, use the margin of your paper to note the appropriate times for inclusion of the visual materials.

PART II: WRITE YOUR SPEECH

Now it is time to write your speech. Remember to apply the rules for writing and delivering a successful speech that you practiced in the first two sections of this book: The First Steps and Putting It into Practice. Put your information in logical order. You might start with facts about the history of the site, telling how the building was used in the past. Write your outline of the speech on this page. (See the activity entitled Using Notecards in The First Steps Section for information about outlining.) On the next page, you will develop the outline into a well-written and well-organized speech.

My Outline:

____

____

____

____

____

____

____

____

Your Tour Guide Speech

PART I: WRITING YOUR SPEECH

As you have learned, all successful speeches have a good beginning, an informative body (middle), and an effective conclusion. Use the notes and outline from the preceding page to help you write your speech. Keep in mind the proper use and timing for visual materials. Make sure your facts are clearly written and easy to follow.

PART II: PRACTICING YOUR SPEECH

A smooth delivery is very important to the success of your talk. Take the time to rehearse your speech. First read the speech aloud several times. Then practice it in front of a mirror so that you can judge your body language. Put your main points on note cards or use your outline and continue to practice. Tape record your talk to help you evaluate your voice. Try your speech out in front of a friend or relative. Be confident and enthusiastic!

You're Invited: A Sample Invitation

Use this sample letter to invite people in your community to the All Around Town culminating activity. Make a class guest list and then divide up the letters you will need to send to family, friends, and people in your school.

Name of School
Class
Address of School
Date

Dear (Name of Guest),

Please join our class on ______________________ for an exciting trip
(Day of Week), (Month), (Date)

around the community of ____________________________________. The students in our class will act as tour guides; each will speak about a different community site. They will enhance their oral presentations with photos, slides, and pictures. We know you will enjoy your day, and hopefully, you will learn more about our town. The community tour will be held in the ____________________ room of our school. We hope to see you there.

Sincerely,

____

Certificate of Participation

____

has participated as a tour guide in *ALL AROUND TOWN*

_______________ date

_______________________________ signature of teacher

Evaluation Form

Complete this evaluation of your activities in the public-speaking experience All Around Town.

1. What new facts did you learn about the town in which you live?

____

____

____

____

____

2. What new skills have you learned as a result of this assignment?

____

____

____

3. Did you feel that the previous experiences prepared you to speak as a "city tour guide"?

____

____

____

____

4. Have your feelings about your hometown changed as a result your participation?

____

____

____

____

5. What, if anything, would you change about the All Around Town assignment?

____

____

____

____

